GLOBAL Songs 2

BREAD FOR THE JOURNEY

Songs of faith, hope, and liberation from the church around the world

Augsburg Fortress

GLOBAL SONGS 2
Bread for the Journey

The publisher gratefully acknowledges all copyright holders who have granted permission to reproduce copyrighted materials in this book. Every effort has been made to determine the owner(s) and/or administrator(s) of each copyright and to secure needed permission. The publisher will, upon written request, make the necessary correction(s) in subsequent printings.

Editors: Frank Stoldt, Lani Willis
Cover art: Pepper Tharp
Cover design: Mike Mihelich
Interior design: Lani Willis

The paper used in this publication meets the minimum requirements of American National Standard for Information Sciences—Permanence of Paper for Printed Materials, ANSI Z329.48-1984.
Printed in the USA. ∞™

11-10813
02   01   00   99   98   ISBN 0-8006-5674-1
                                                          2   3   4   5   6   7   8   9   10

Songs of faith, hope, and liberation from

Africa

Latin America and the Caribbean

North America

Europe and Asia

Christ Has Arisen, Alleluia

Text: Bernard Kyamanywa, trans. Howard S. Olson © 1977 Howard S. Olson. Used by permission.
Music: traditional Tanzanian

Let us sing praise to him with end - less joy.

Death's fear - ful sting he has come to de - stroy.

Our sin for - giv - ing, al - le - lu - ia!

Je - sus is liv - ing, al - le - lu - ia!

Hamba Nathi

Text and tune: traditional South African
Arr. Anders Nyberg, © Utryck, admin. Walton Music Corp.
English text: Gerhard Cartford, © Lutheran World Federation. Used by permission.

Additional English verses:

Listen to us, our sorrow is great.
Come talk with us, give meaning in life.
Come eat with us, and share in our bread.
Come stay with us, for evening is nigh.

Reamo leboga
(To God our thanks we give)

Re-a - mo le - bo - ga, re-a - mo le - bo - ga,
To God our thanks we give, to God our thanks we give,

re-a - mo le - bo - ga mo-di - mo wa ro - na.
to God our thanks we give, our thanks to God we give.

Text and tune: traditional Botswanan, as taught by Daisy Nshakazongwe © 1986 World Council of Churches and the Asian Institute for Liturgy and Music. Used and adapted by permission.
English paraphrase (adapted) and notation: I-to Loh.

Mayenziwe
(Your will be done)

Text: from the Lord's Prayer
Music: traditional South African

Sizohamba naye
(We will go with God)

Si - zo - ham - ba na - ye! Ho, ho! ho! Si - zo - ham - ba na - ye! ye!
We will go with God! Ho, ho, ho! We will go with God! God!

Ngo-mhla, ho!
This day, oh!

Ngo- mhla we - nja - bu - lo si - zo - ha - mba na - ye.
On this day of great joy we will go with God

Ngo- mhla, ho!
This day, oh!

Ngo- mhla we - nja bu - lo si - zo - ha - mba na - ye.
On this day of great joy we will go with God.

Text and tune: traditional South African
Arr. Dave Darvie © Dave Darvie, South Africa. Used by permission.

10 ✤ South Africa

Amen. Alleluia!

Text: traditional
Music: traditional South African

Thuma mina

(Send me, Jesus)

1 Thu - ma mi - na, thu - ma mi - na, thu - ma mi - na, Nko - si yam.
2 Ndi - ya vu - ma, ndi - ya vu - ma, ndi - ya vu - ma, Nko - si yam.

1 Send me, Je - sus; send me, Je - sus; send me, Je - sus; send me, Lord.
2 I am will - ing; I am will-ing; I am will - ing, will - ing, Lord.

Cantor

Thu - ma mi-na

Text and music: traditional South African

Sanna, sannanina

San- na,   san- na- ni- na,   san- na,   san- na, san- na,   san-

na,   san- na,   san - na,   san- na- ni- na,   san- na,   san- na, san- na.   San - na.

Sanna means "hosanna."

Text and tune: traditional South African
Arr. Betty Pulkingham © 1975 Celebration, admin. in USA and Canada by The Copyright Company. All rights reserved.

Come, the Banquet Hall Is Ready

Waltz tempo

1 Come, the ban-quet hall is rea-dy, pre-par-a-tions are com-plete.
2 We ac-cept the way of Je-sus when we eat the bread and wine;
3 How can we be-gin to thank you for this sac-ri-fice of love;
4 This is how we wish to thank you for the life you free-ly give:

Christ him-self has spread the ta-ble, see how lav-ish is the feast.
he who gave his life for oth-ers, at his ta-ble we will dine.
for this great and gen-tle mys-tery: giv-ing up your-self as food.
we will fol-low your ex-am-ple in the way we choose to live.

Ev- 'ry-one has been in-vit-ed, there's e-nough to go a-round.
He is liv-ing still a-mong us in the peo-ple seek-ing truth.
Food to fill a starv-ing peo-ple long-ing for a bet-ter day.
We will share with one an-oth-er, we will not let jus-tice wait.

Text and tune: Guillermo Cuéllar, trans. Bret Hesla and Bill Dexheimer Pharris © GIA Publications, Inc. All rights reserved. Used by permission.
Arr. Bread for the Journey © 1997 Augsburg Fortress

Here the sweet-est bread is giv-en, here the fin-est wine is found.
He is liv-ing in our strug-gles, in the righ-teous things we do.
Or - gan - iz - ing with their neigh-bors, strug - gling to find their way.
We will sow the seeds of free-dom in the ash - es of the hate.

Here the sweet-est bread is giv-en, here the fin-est wine is found.
He is liv-ing in our strug-gles, in the righ-teous things we do.
Or - gan - iz - ing with their neigh-bors, strug - gling to find their way.
We will sow the seeds of free-dom in the ash - es of the hate.

Huapango (more upbeat)

God, we're hun-gry for an hon - est wage, for hous-ing, and for bread.

Streng-then   us   with this com - mun - ion   for the strug-gles still a -

head.   for   the strug-gles still a - head.

Come to Be Our Hope, O Jesus

Text and music: Jaci Maraschin © 1978 Jaci Maraschin, Sao Paulo, Brazil.
English text © 1989 World Council of Churches. Used by permission.

nei - ros   da_in - jus - ti - ça_e da_a - fli - ção;   vem, re -
pris - on   those who   suf - fer in   our land.   In your
mor - row   for a   King - dom, now   so near.   Take a -

E   A   G#7   C#m   E7

ú - ne_os bra - si - lei - ros   em a - mor   e_emcom-preen - são.
love   we find   the rea - son   still to   live   and un - der - stand.
way   all hu - man sor - row,   give us   hope   a- gainst our   fear.

A   B   E   C   Am   B   E

2   Vem tecer um mundo novo nos caminhos da verdade;
     para que, afinal, o povo viva em plen liberdade.
     Vem, Jesus, abre o futuro do teu reino de algeria.
     Vem, derruba o imenso muro que separa a noite e o dia.

Sarantañani

Text and tune: Zoilo Chambi © 1991 Zoilo Chambi, La Paz, Bolivia.
English para. Bret Hesla; Arr. Bread for the Journey
English text and arr. © 1997 Augsburg Fortress

Miren qué bueno

Refrain

Mir - en qué bue - no qué bue - no es. es.
Be - hold, how plea - sant, how good it is! is!

1 Mi - ren qué bue - no_es cuan - do to - do_el pue - blo es - tá jun - to.
1 How plea - sant and har - mon - ious when God's peo - ple are to - geth - er.

es co mo_a-cei - te bue - no de - rra - ma - do so - bre_Aa - rón.
Fra - grant as pre - cious oil when run - ning fresh on Aa - ron's beard.

2 *Miren qué bueno es cuando todo el pueblo está junto:*
   se parace al rocio sobre los montes de Síon.
2 How pleasant and harmonious when God's people are together:
   refreshing as the dew upon the mountain of the Lord.

3 *Miren qué bueno es cuando todo el pueblo está junto:*
   porque el Señor ahi manda vida eterna y benedición.
3 How pleasant and harmonious when God's people are together:
   there the Lord God bestows a blessing—life forevermore.

Text: Psalm 133, adapt. Pablo Sosa; tune: Pablo Sosa
Text and tune © Pablo Sosa, Camacuá 252, 1406 Buenos Aires, Argentina. Used by permission.
Arr. Bread for the Journey © 1997 Augsburg Fortress

Argentina ✣ 21

The Right Hand of God

Text: Patrick Prescod © Caribbean Conference of Churches, West Indies.
Tune: Noel Dexter © Caribbean Conference of Churches, West Indies.
Arr. Bread for the Journey © 1997 Augsburg Fortress

tears   are   re - cord - ed   by   the   right   hand   of
stray,   but   we're   guid - ed   by   the   right   hand   of
just   are   de - stroyed   by   the   right   hand   of
shame   by   the   lift - ing   of   the   right   hand   of
much,   when we're   healed   by   the   right   hand   of

F   Gm7   F/A   B♭   Adim   Gm   F/C   C

To stanzas   *Last time*

God.
God.
God.
God.
God.

F

By the Waters of Babylon

Text: Psalm 137
Tune: traditional Jamaican
Arr. Bread for the Journey © 1997 Augsburg Fortress

How can we sing our ho - ly song in a strange land? For the wick-ed

land? So let the words of my mouth and the med-i - ta-tions of my

heart, be ac - cep-ta-ble in your sight, O God.

I Shall Walk in the Presence of God

I shall walk in the pres-ence of God. I shall walk.

With the sun and the rain up-on me I shall walk.

In the land of the liv-ing, liv - ing land I shall walk.

Text and tune: Larry Dittberner © 1990 Larry Dittberner. Used by permission.
Arr. Bread for the Journey © 1997 Augsburg Fortress

With my sis- ters and bro - thers a- round me I shall walk.

I shall walk.

Additional verses:
    I shall sing ...
    I shall pray ...
    I shall breathe ...
    I shall dance ...

A Dazzling Bouquet

Big Backbeat

Refrain

Mine is the church where ev-'ry-bod-y's wel-come.
1 Come here, all you six - foot glad - i - o-las;
2 We don't sim - ply tol - er - ate each oth - er;
3 Our de - mons keep try - ing to di - vide us;

I know it's true 'cause I got through the door.
come, all you pur - ple li - lacs shin - ing bright.
we ask and tell; we don't just turn a - way.
they doc - u - ment their lies to make them true.

Text and tune: Bret Hesla © 1995 Bret Hesla, admin. Augsburg Fortress
Arr. Bread for the Journey © 1997 Augsburg Fortress

We are a dazz - ling bou-quet of ev - 'ry kind of flow-er.
Come, let us all bloom to-geth - er in the gar-den:
We give at - ten - tion to ev - 'ry bud and blos-som.
To - day we're freed from our judg - ing and ex - clu-ding.

A7

Jump in the vase, 'cause we've got space for more.
a car - ni - val of fra-grance and de - light.
Let ev - 'ry face come grace the grand bou-quet.
Just look a-round, en - joy the love - ly view.

D

Come, Let Us Worship God

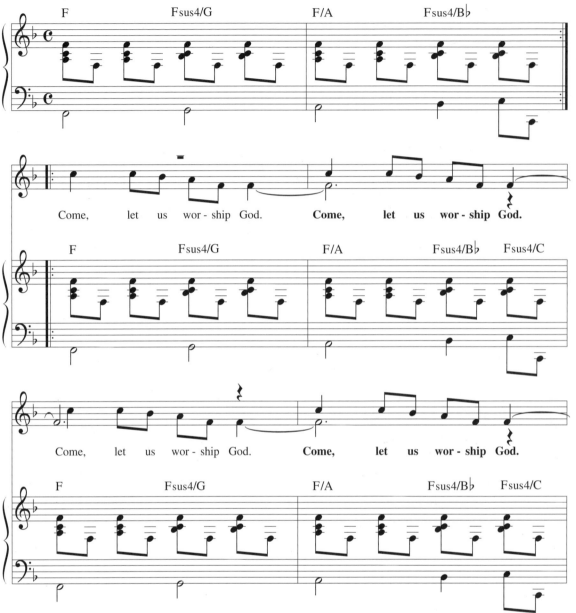

Come, let us wor-ship God. **Come,** **let us wor-ship God.**

Come, let us wor-ship God. **Come,** **let us wor-ship God.**

Text and tune: Ray Makeever © 1983 Ray Makeever, admin. Augsburg Fortress
Arr. Tom Witt © 1997 Augsburg Fortress

Additional verses: Rest for the weary . . .
Food for the hungry . . .
Hope for the children, etc.

Let Us Put On the Clothes of Christ

Refrain

Let us put on the clothes of Christ and live as e-quals with ev- 'ry-one. Let us

put on the clothes of Christ and re-u-nite the fam- 'ly of God.

To stanzas

Last time

Leader

All

1 Jew and Greek will live side by side
2 All the cap - tives will be set free   with the gar-ments of jus-tice on.
3 Men and wom - en will live as one
4 Let us rise up com - plete - ly new

Dis -

Text and tune: Bret Hesla © 1993 Bret Hesla, admin. Augsburg Fortress
Arr. Bread for the Journey © 1997 Augsburg Fortress

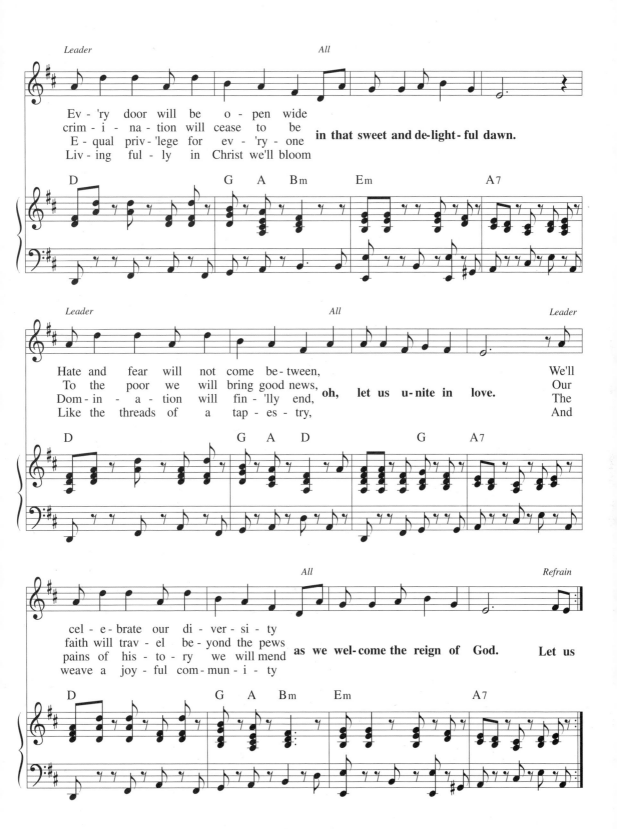

Leader ... *All*

Ev - 'ry door will be o - pen wide
crim - i - na - tion will cease to be
E - qual priv - 'lege for ev - 'ry - one
Liv - ing ful - ly in Christ we'll bloom

in that sweet and de-light-ful dawn.

D G A Bm Em A7

Leader ... *All* ... *Leader*

Hate and fear will not come be - tween,
To the poor we will bring good news,
Dom - in - a - tion will fin - 'lly end,
Like the threads of a tap - es - try,

oh, let us u - nite in love.

We'll
Our
The
And

D G A D G A7

All ... *Refrain*

cel - e - brate our di - ver - si - ty
faith will trav - el be - yond the pews
pains of his - to - ry we will mend
weave a joy - ful com - mun - i - ty

as we wel-come the reign of God.

Let us

D G A Bm Em A7

Everything that We Have

Swing time, with backbeat

Refrain

Ev - 'ry-
1 Work - ing
2 May we

thing that we have, ev - 'ry - thing that we are, ev - 'ry
hard to sur - vive is no guar - an-tee, for the
show grat - i - tude in the way that we live, not with

mo-ment is a bless-ing from a - bove. It's end-less
deck is al - ways stacked a-gainst the poor. If we'd use
pom-pous prayers and not with fan - cy feasts. I - ma-gine

Text and tune: Bret Hesla © 1989 Bret Hesla, admin. Augsburg Fortress
Arr. Bread for the Journey © 1997 Augsburg Fortress

love that we breathe, it's end-less love that we re-ceive.
just what we need, re-ject the creep-ing can-cer of greed,
how the world should be, then take a risk to build this dream:

What has free-ly come we now let free-ly go.
like a mir-a-cle the hun-gry could be fed.
that's the of-fer-ing that God is ask-ing for.

To stanzas or refrain

Last time

Ev-'ry
1 Work-ing
2 May we

Go Tell It on the Mountain

Go tell it on the moun - tain o - ver the hills and ev - 'ry-where;

To Interlude, ad lib

Go tell it on the moun - tain that Je - sus Christ is born!

Text and tune: traditional African American
Arr. Tom Witt © 1997 Augsburg Fortress

1 While shep - herds kept their watch - ing o'er
2 The shep - herds feared and trem - bled when,
3 Down in a lone - ly man - ger the

si - lent flocks by night, be - hold, through - out the
lo, a - bove the earth rang out the an - gel
hum - ble Christ was born; and God sent us sal -

heav - ens there shone a ho - ly light._____
cho - rus that hailed our Sav - ior's birth._____
va - tion that bless - ed Christ - mas morn._____

Refrain

Heleluyan

He - le - lu - yan, he - le - lu - yan; he - le, he - le - lu - yan;

he - le - lu - yan, he - le - lu - yan; he - le, he - le - lu - yan.

Text and tune: Muscogee (Creek) Indian
Transcription: Charles Webb © 1989 The United Methodist Publishing House. Used by permission.

Bread for the Journey

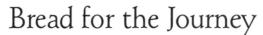

Freely

bread	for	the	jour-ney,	give us	bread.	Give us
way	as	we	trav-el,	guide our	way.	Guide our
one	with	each	oth-er,	make us	one.	Make us
home	to	the	gar-den,	lead us	home.	Lead us

1,5 Give us
2 Guide our
3 Make us
4 Lead us

bread   for   the   jour- ney,   give   us   bread.   When   our
way   as   we   trav- el,   guide   our   way.   With   so
one   with   each   oth- er,   make   us   one.   All   the
home   to   the   gar- den,   lead   us   home;   where   we'll

Bm   Bm/A   E/G♯   G   A

legs   are   get- ting   heav- y,   and   we're   hang- ing   down   our   heads,   give   us
ma-   ny   roads   be- fore   us,   where   to   go   is   hard   to   say.   Guide   our
walls   we've   built   a- round   us: may   we   learn   to   tear   them   down.   Make   us
live   with   all   cre- a- tion,   find   our   place   and   nev- er   roam.   Lead   us

Bm   Bm/A   Em   G

8vb

bread   for   the   jour- ney,   give   us   bread.
way   as   we   trav- el,   guide   our   way.
one   with   each   oth- er,   make   us   one.
home   to   the   gar- den,   lead   us   home.

D   G   D

When Twilight Comes

1 When twi- light comes and the sun sets, moth- er hen pre- pares for
2 One day the Rab- bi, Lord Je - sus, called the twelve to share his
3 So gath- er 'round once a - gain, friends, touched by fad- ing glow of

night's rest. As her brood shel- ters un - der her wings she
last meal. As the hen tends her young, so for them he
sun's gold, and re - count all our frail hu- man hopes: the

gives the love of God to her nest. Oh! what joy to
spent him - self to seek and to heal. Oh! what joy to
dreams of young and sto- ries of old. Oh! what joy to

feel her warm heart - beat and be near her all night long;
be with Christ Je - sus, hear his voice, oh! sheer de - light,
pray close to - geth - er, kneel- ing as one fam- i - ly,

Text: Moises Andrade; trans. James Minchin © James Minchin, admin. Asian Institute for Liturgy and Music. Used by permission.
Music: Francisco Feliciano © Francisco Feliciano

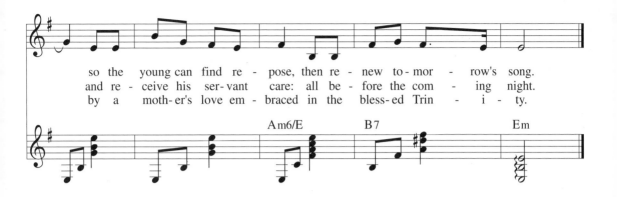

so the   young can find re - pose, then re - new to - mor - row's song.
and re - ceive his ser-vant   care: all be - fore the com - ing night.
by a   moth-er's love em - braced in the   bless-ed Trin - i - ty.

Day by Day

Text: Carolina Sandell Berg; trans. Robert Leaf © 1992 Augsburg Fortress
Tune: Oskar Ahnfelt
Arr. Bread for the Journey © 1997 Augsburg Fortress

vine, be-yond all mor-tal meas - ure, brings to naught the bur-dens of my
fear no e - vil of the mor - row, I will trust in your en - dur-ing
day, no mat-ter what be - tide me, you will hold me ev - er in your

Eb   Eb/G   Ab9   Bb

quest; Sav - ior, lead me to the home I trea - sure, where at
grace. Sav - ior, help me bear life's pain and sor - row till in
hand. Sav - ior, with your pres-ence here to guide me, I will

Eb   Eb   Eb/G   Ab9

last I'll find e - ter - nal rest.
glo - ry I be - hold your face.
reach at last the pro - mised land.

Bb7   Eb

Canticle of the Turning

1 My soul cries out with a joy-ful shout that the God of my heart is
2 Though I am small, my God, my all, you work great things in
3 From the halls of power to the for-tress tower, not a stone will be left on
4 Though the na-tions rage from age to age, we re-mem-ber who holds us

great, and my spir-it sings of the won-drous things that you bring to the ones who
me, and your mer-cy will last from the depths of the past to the end of the age to
stone. Let the king be-ware for your jus-tice tears ev-'ry ty-rant from his
fast: God's mer-cy must de-liv-er us from the con-quer-or's crush-ing

wait. You fixed your sight on your ser-vant's plight, and my weak-ness you did not
be. Your ver-y name puts the proud to shame, and to those who would for you
throne. The hun-gry poor shall weep no more, for the food they can nev-er
grasp. This sav-ing word that our fore-bears heard is the prom-ise which holds us

Tune: STAR OF THE COUNTY DOWN, traditional Irish
Text and arr.: Rory Cooney © 1990 GIA Publications, Inc. All rights reserved. Used by permission.

46 ✤ Ireland/USA

spurn, so from east to west shall my name be blest. Could the world be a-bout to
yearn, you will show your might, put the strong to flight, for the world is a-bout to
earn; there are ta-bles spread, ev-'ry mouth be fed, for the world is a-bout to
bound, 'til the spear and rod can be crushed by God, who is turn-ing the world a-

D   Em   G   D   Em   C

turn?
turn.   My heart shall sing of the day you bring. Let the fires of your jus-tice
turn.
round.

Em   G   D   Em   C

burn. Wipe a-way all tears, for the dawn draws near, and the world is a-bout to turn.

D   Em   C   D   Em   C   Em

Oi Jumalan Karitsa

Text and music: Matti Rantatalo © 1992 Matti Rantatalo. Used by permission.
Trans.: International Commission on English in the Liturgy, alt.

Come Now, O Prince of Peace

O - so - so   o - so - so,   pyong - hwa - ui - im - gum
1 Come now, O Prince of peace, make us one bod - y.
2 Come now, O God of love, make us one bod - y.
3 Come now and set us free, O God, our Sav - ior.
4 Come, Hope of u - ni - ty, make us one bod - y.

u - ri - ga   han - mom   i - ru - ge   ha - so - so.
Come, O Lord Je - sus, re - con - cile your peo - ple.
Come, O Lord Je - sus, re - con - cile your peo - ple.
Come, O Lord Je - sus, re - con - cile all na - tions.
Come, O Lord Je - sus, re - con - cile all na - tions.

Text: Geonyong Lee; English para.: Marion Pope
Tune: O-SO-SO, traditional Korean
Arr. Geonyong Lee © 1991 Geonyong Lee. Used by permission.

Background Notes

Bread for the Journey

Bret Hesla wrote this prayer in 1992 while participating in a series of weekly, metro-wide ecumenical Lenten services held at St. Stephen's Roman Catholic Church in Minneapolis, Minn. The series, which was called "Bread for the Journey," focused on fostering solidarity among Christians whose faith is interwoven with a commitment to building a just world. St. Stephen's was a good choice for the location, because the congregation has been a leader in grounding their faith in acts of concrete opposition to urban injustices. Their long-standing shelter for the homeless is one of the places of hope in the Phillips neighborhood of Minneapolis.

Sometimes Bret uses verse one as a chorus. His friend Larry and Larry's sister Janet do this song slowed way down, about half of the tempo, which is already slow. If you've got the lungs, give it a try.

By the Waters of Babylon

This version of Psalm 133 is based on an old Rastafarian chant from Jamaica. Rastafarians, who regard themselves as Black Israelites, compare Jamaica to Babylon, a land of exile and social and spiritual oppression, and long for a return to Zion (Africa). Beyond the Caribbean context, this psalm text speaks clearly for many refugees and displaced people in our world today. The lamenting cries, combined with the Caribbean rhythms of this setting, make for a rather startling juxtaposition of tune and text. This is a prime example of how in the music of many cultures, laments are sung not just to dirges, but also, on occasion, to more lively rhythmic tunes.

Using a song leader to "call" the three sections (and even to sing all the way through each of them first) helps an assembly join in. We often use this song to illustrate some simple Afro-Caribbean rhythms that untrained percussionists—like many of us!—can use.

Canticle of the Turning

Standing in the long tradition of hymns that combine biblical texts and secular tunes, Rory Cooney has paired Mary's Magnificat with this Irish tune, "Star of the County Down," which might be more commonly heard in a tavern! Contrary to the sweeter, gentler melodies we normally hear with this text, this tune gives power and energy to Mary's strong words of wonder, praise, and prophecy that God is indeed turning the world around.

This can be accompanied by guitar, mandolin, fiddle, penny whistle, or with just a piano. Whatever you do, don't let it drag. Be sure to maintain the sense of rolling energy encouraged by both the tune and text. Especially with a song like this, it takes until the third or fourth run-through to be able to feel the rhythm and movement without stumbling over the words.

Christ Has Arisen, Alleluia

Lutheran missionary Howard Olson's work with seminary students in Tanzania has given us a number of great songs, including this lively Easter hymn. This hymn sounds good with combined adult, youth and children's choirs. Steady, simple percussion (with a definite 2 against 3 clave beat) keeps it lively. Think about using a smaller choir for the verses and the assembly for the refrain.

Come, Let Us Worship God

God's people are gathering for worship. Some have been in the sanctuary for awhile, sitting silently, praying. Others are just arriving, shaking hands, sharing words of greeting. Some are busy finding things to keep their children occupied. A few are thumbing through their hymn books. A couple of newcomers are wondering where to sit. Out of their midst comes a solo voice (either a capella or with piano) singing, "Come, let us worship God." Attention shifts from individual thoughts and activities as the people respond with one voice, "Come, let us worship God." Then they hear, "Welcome, everyone, to the love of God," and they all respond in kind, proclaiming the intention of their togetherness, maybe even reaching out hands of welcome to each other as they continue singing back and forth, naming the great gifts of love: rest for the weary, food for the hungry, hope for the children.

Printed music and words are not necessary for this piece. You can introduce it by simply inviting people to sing back what is sung to them. Additional verses may be written to fit the season or the particular worshipping context.

Come Now, O Prince of Peace

This prayer, based on 2 Corinthians 5:17-20, was originally composed for an historic meeting that took place between Christians from North and South Korea. In fact, when sung in a Korean context, the word used for "reconciliation" would immediately bring to mind the reunification of those two countries. This hymn also lends itself to use as a response to a litany or during the prayers of the people, and is particularly appropriate during the season of Advent.

Even though it's unlikely that non-native speakers would be able to perfectly intone the subtle differences in a few of these Korean syllables, don't let that discourage you! With a little coaching, the Korean is possible to sing, especially for a choir, with the congregation following in English.

A single treble instrument, such as a flute or a violin, can play through the melody first, then use voices in unison for verses one and two. Although it would be unusual for a traditional Korean tune to be harmonized in four parts like this, European and American influences have traveled far and we have a lovely cross-cultural sound in this hymn. Keep your accompanying instrument light—you don't really need much. It may be a good time to try out a harp or koto sound on your synthesizer, if you have one.

Come to Be Our Hope, O Jesus

These words by Jaci Maraschin are sung to several different tunes in Brazil, including the one we've chosen. We never seem to get tired of Maraschin's Advent text that speaks of Jesus' coming not just to save individual sinners, but to liberate peoples and nations from oppression of all kinds, and to usher in a new era of shalom. The church needs to sing about this larger vision of hope!

This song is to be done in the *baião* style, which has its roots in the northeastern part of Brazil. It is influenced by the African circle dance and typically includes the blues sound you hear in this song. Traditionally, you would hear a triangle, a tambourine, a large drum, and an accordion. On our recording we altered the instrumentation, but kept the blues/dance rhythm going with harmonica, guitar, synthesizer, and percussion. This song can be accompanied quite simply on the piano. Remember to keep a steady, dance-like feel.

Come, the Banquet Hall Is Ready

Guillermo Cúellar wrote this as part of the *Salvadoran Campesino Mass,* commissioned by Archbishop Oscar Romero, who soon after was assassinated during the very act of administering the sacraments. Later, Guillermo was exiled from his own country for more than ten years because of threats on his own life. The shared meal of which he speaks is no doubt a threat to those powerful who try to hoard God's gifts for themselves.

We find that singing this communion song deepens and radicalizes our understanding of the eucharist here in North America, as well. A woman recently came up to us and thanked us deeply for using it at a church assembly. She said, "When I hear people singing that they're hungry for an honest wage, for housing, and for bread, I really start to believe that I'm part of a new church!"

There are two distinct rhythms in this song. The verse is similar to a waltz. The chorus changes to a traditional Mexican *huapango* rhythm, which isn't necessarily faster, but has a different bass line and percussive feel, as you can hear on our recording. Traditionally, this song would be led by "people's" instruments—guitar, accordion, violin, drum, and voice.

Day by Day

Gracia Grindal writes: "Caroline Sandell was the daughter of a Swedish Lutheran pastor in Smaland. Through the years she suffered many tragedies, not the least the loss of her father in a boating accident. She became an active participant in revivals of the day. Active as a writer and editor of a Christian magazine, she achieved an affectionate place in the hearts of Swedes everywhere for her warm Christian hymns and songs. Oskar Ahnfelt, known as the 'evangelical troubadour of Sweden,' was always eager to set her texts to tunes he could sing and play on his ten-stringed guitar. This most popular Sandell song was written after she had heard the story of a clock pendulum complaining to the clock hand that it did not have the strength to tick a billion more times. The hand said comfortingly, you only have to tick once more— 'As thy day is, so shall thy strength be.'

"Songs like 'Day by Day'—those known in European and European-American churches as spiritual songs or gospel songs—were often relegated to youth songbooks, or some place other than the official Sunday morning worship books. It's a good thing that some of these old favorites are now being included in newer hymnals because: 1) as families, we don't do as much singing together outside of Sunday morning worship and these songs could be lost for good; and 2) they are often treasured 'heart songs,' helping to form and shape our faith."

This tune is particularly beautiful and can be sung together quite simply in unison with a guitar or piano accompanying. It is also lovely in two, three or four parts (for harmonies, see a version in *With One Voice*), either a capella or with an unobtrusive instrumental accompaniment.

A Dazzling Bouquet

This is a song to celebrate inclusivity in the church. A growing number of congregations in various denominations are taking a stand to welcome gay and lesbian people into their membership. We hope this song can help encourage and support that movement.

This is a dance tune: Listen to some Zydeco music to get the back-beat feel. Accordion, fiddle, trap set, washboard, and triangle would be great, but, as always, use what you've got.

Everything that We Have

Christians are sometimes torn between thinking we really should 'give every-thing away' and thinking that's just a metaphor for an attitude we need. One seems too idealistic, the other an easy rationalization. Actually, gratitude is more than attitude—it's a lifestyle, a standard of living. The verses were added several years after the song had left home, following a friend's comment, "Get some verses and that would be a nice song." We still can't decide how we like it best, with or without verses, for adding all those words can result in a loss of layers of meaning. Suit yourself, but feel free to use only the refrain.

Remember to use swing-time rhythm—don't play straight eighth notes. Also, it would be nice to add a trap set. Attention improvisers! The old revival tune, "Just as I Am without one Plea" fits almost perfectly over this chord pat-tern. You just have to make two adjustments: stretch the song out from 3/4 to 4/4, and change the chord for the word "plea"—go back to the root chord (G). It even harmonizes nicely when played on top of the "Everything" melody. Try using a solo instrument (saxophone, perhaps?) on this tune as an interlude between verses.

Go Tell It On the Mountain

Tom Witt's arrangement of this Christmas classic rejuvenates the hymn for us today. This arrangement is ideal for four-part choirs, with clapping on 2 and 4. It's best to try and find (or encourage amongst yourselves!) a gospel-style soloist who can improvise on the verses.

Hamba Nathi

This is another of those South African freedom songs that have been collected by Anders Nyberg of Sweden, though, as far as we know, it hasn't yet had much exposure in North America. The original Zulu text can be translated, "Come walk with us, our liberator."

If you're teaching this to a group, memorize all the parts first, and then throw away the music—it's much easier to learn by ear. The harmonies are predictable, repetitive, and very accessible to a good singing group. Only the voices are needed, along with some clapping and dancing, of course. During the second half of the piece, it is possible to add a second choral part (same words and notes) that quickly echoes the first choral part, staggered by one quarter note. (We didn't write it in because it looks more confusing than it really is!)

Heleluyan

It has been suggested that you might also accompany this simple alleluia with the out-of-tempo beating of a hand drum, which might be done with some traditional Native American songs. Find a recording that could help you hear this style of singing and drumming.

I Shall Walk in the Presence of God

Larry Dittberner is a St. Paul, Minn. musician and a Montessori music teacher. He is also a member of St. Frances Cabrini Roman Catholic Church, where he has led Sunday worship services for 30 years. Each month Larry takes the assigned psalm and makes a new song that the congregation can sing (and dance) to. Larry is an accomplished songleader, able to loosen even the stiffest of groups into a singing, swaying mass of joy. Like most of his songs, "I Shall Walk" reflects his commitment to an earthy spirituality and the tough work of building lasting community. As Larry put it, "'sisters and brothers' in this song refers not only to people, but also to birds, rocks, trees, stars, and all of God's creation."

This is a zipper song, as Pete Seeger would say: you can call out a different word and zip out a whole new verse ("I shall _____ in the presence of God"). If you add a few measures of vamping between verses, you can also get members of the congregation or audience to call out ideas. It's a good way to be surprised, like the time we were singing with a group of kids and someone called out "play video games." (There's a theological challenge!) This song is also a good opportunity to pass out percussion instruments and invite people to play some simple rhythms. If you have access to experienced percussionists, ask them if they'd be willing to teach some simple repeating patterns to a volunteer percussion choir in a pre-service practice.

Let Us Put on the Clothes of Christ

The group Bread for the Journey evolved out of a collection of musicians helping to provide music for a handful of global mission events of the Evangelical Lutheran Church in America (ELCA) in the early 1990s. The theme for the summer of 1993 was taken from the Galatians text, and the planners asked for a song about it. While working on the song, Bret Hesla happened to attend an anti-racism workshop. One comment he remembers someone making during a session was that we long for a dropping of all the separateness and fear, to be reunited with the entire human family, the entire family of God.

You probably need to teach this one in advance, or at least talk through it. The call/response structure of the verses is a little complicated, in that there are four different responses per verse. However, these responses remain the same despite the changing calls in the succeeding verses.

Miren qué bueno

We find ourselves using this psalm setting by Pablo Sosa quite often. Not only does it serve as a good gathering song, but it's also an easy way to lead non-Spanish speaking people in singing Spanish. The Spanish words are easy and repetitive. We recommend having the assembly sing only the refrain in Spanish (as on the recording) and a cantor (or two) sing the verses in Spanish and/or English. If you have an electronic keyboard, now is the time to try out the marimba setting; otherwise a piano or a guitar will do, especially if it's accompanied by some simple rhythms as you hear on our recording.

Oi Jumalan Karitsa

This *Lamb of God* is one piece from the larger *Thomas Mass,* composed in 1992 as part of an effort to revitalize the Finnish church. The mass is now done regularly on Sunday nights at a large cathedral in Helsinki and draws in hundreds of young people. Once you teach the Finnish, it's actually quite easy to sing in the original language. Find someone who knows Finnish (or a relative language like Estonian) and teach it to everyone!

The Right Hand of God

This is a popular hymn from the Caribbean, composed for the Inaugural Assembly of the Caribbean Conference of Churches in Jamaica in 1973. There is a sixth verse we didn't include on our recording, because it seemed more appropriately sung by a Caribbean congregation:

> 6. The right hand of God is planting in our land,
>   planting seeds of freedom, hope, and love.
>   In these Caribbean lands, let his people all join hands,
>   and be one with the right hand of God.

If you have access to a percussionist, she/he will know how to build the calypso rhythm it deserves.

Sanna, sannanina

This short response is said to have come from South Africa, but we've also seen it attributed to Tanzania and sung in Swahili.

This exclamation of praise (Hosanna to the Most High!) can be used effectively in liturgy as either a response to a litany, or by itself as a song of adoration. To get it started, it may be easier if a single voice sings the first "Sanna, sannanina" as a call, with everyone joining in parts at the beginning of the second measure.

Sarantañani

The language in which the song was written is of the Aymara people in Bolivia, South America. John Bell of the Iona Community (Scotland), writes that the Aymara "took over the Methodist church and indigenised it. This kind of crisis for the church is what must be expected if you speak about the rights of native people." The English text is more of a paraphrase than a translation of the original.

We prefer to teach this song (at least the English paraphrase) without using any printed text, in a call and response fashion; the assembly can easily sing back what they hear the leader call out. The song has a dance rhythm, so if you can't get people to actually dance, it would be appropriate to have them move as they sing—especially given the text that calls us to move together! Try using a simple side-to-side step: step together, step together; repeat in the other direction. The song can also be used for a procession.

Southern African medley

Tom Witt put these six pieces together on the recording, creating a medley of typical southern African hymnody. The languages are Xhosa, Zulu, and Tswana. Normally they would be used separately (and repeated quite a few times!) as hymns and responses of thanks and praise. Just about all of them have additional verses that have been written along the way. This particular version of "Thuma Mina" is different from the one found in most USA denominational hymnals these days, but it is actually much more widely sung within South Africa. We didn't include the music for "Siyahamba" in this songbook because of its widespread availability in newer denominational hymnals. All of the songs are to be sung a cappella, with optional percussion, as you can hear on the recording.

When Twilight Comes

Composer Francisco Feliciano describes music as "sound moving in space, like birds in flight." That image helped us to think of this tune as a bird moving freely in space, and then gently landing on a branch to rest before taking off again. The last half of the song Feliciano describes as a "descending scale of golden notes" (with the birds landing on B, A, G, F#, and E). Wedded with this beautiful tune is a wonderful Lenten text that incorporates feminine imagery of God that we find glaringly absent in much hymnody.

The hymn can be presented very simply with a flute or violin playing the tune once through. If a guitarist is available, she/he can strum the chords as marked. Have a cantor or choir sing the first verse and then invite the congregation to join. Keep the voices unison throughout.

–Notes by Bread for the Journey

Scriptural Index

Geographical/Cultural Index

Topical Index

Alphabetical Index